·A CASTLE IN FAIRYLAND·

and other stories
of The Carson Family and their Mansions

Inspired by Papa's Day Book
and
Written by His Daughter

Evelyn Shuster Worthen

5th Printing

2808 Fairfield
Eureka, CA 95501
(707) 442-9220

Printed by
Eureka Printing Company, Inc.
106 T Street
Eureka, CA 95501

William Carson

Dedicated to my writing friends in the Creative Writing Group sponsored by Gayle Karshner of R.S.V.P. Humboldt State University. To Gayle, Melba Bosch, Jessie Carlson, Margaret Delaney, Grace Dixon, Zelma Gabbert, Clara Holloway, Evelyn Mansfield and Alice Palmgren, my thanks and appreciation for your encouragement and constructive criticism. I could not have done it without you. Special thanks to Jessie Carlson for typing my manuscript, and to my brother, Merle Shuster, for his excellent photography.

THE DAY BOOK

INTRODUCTION

A page from Papa's Day Book.

t all began after Papa died in 1948, when my brother Merle Shuster and I became interested in Papa's Day Books. They were meticulously kept from Dec. 1900 to June, 1930, recording work days, number of hours, and pay received. I went through the Day Books many times, wishing he had written more than just the bare accounts of his work and expenditures. But he was not keeping a diary as I have done for 25 years. And so many are the questions I would like to have asked him. However, when I came across references to his work in "The Castle," as Papa called the famed Carson Mansion, I became greatly interested. I carefully traced the record of his work, first for William Carson, owner of the Mansion, then for Milton, his oldest son who moved into the home after his father's death, and finally for Sumner, the second son who later built his own mansion, and for whom Papa worked for nearly 35 years.

His work at "The Castle" began in May 1911 when he washed 17 windows for $1.75. It took him 5 hours. The mansion had been completed in 1886, so it was now 25 years old.

He began his work at Sumner's Mansion on the corner of 7th and "J" in June, 1914, when the home was new. At that time he washed 31 windows for $3.10. His total time was 5½ hours. But the entry that really aroused my interest read as follows:

Feb. 21, 1912—tolled the bell for the Carson funeral
1¾ hours—60¢

From that concise account came the story of "The Bell Ringer," included in this book.

Now my curiosity was greatly stimulated as I looked back into the past and realized that with my inside information enriched with added research, I might write some interesting stories, hitherto unpublished. Today Papa's Day Book has inspired me to do just that.

Many articles and books have been written about the original Carson Mansion, now the Ingomar Club. Most of them have been impersonal, and many of a descriptive type. Few have entered into the private lives of those living inside the Mansion. In my stories, I have endeavored to portray the family life of those involved in the Carson story. Having a more particular insight into the home of the second son, Sumner Charles, through the long association of my father as a housekeeper in the Sumner Mansion, I have centered my thoughts around him. Beginning with Sumner's boyhood and tracing his life into adulthood, I have sought to produce the flavor of life in a millionaire's family. Seeking to be historically correct, I have inserted only a few of my imaginative thoughts, simply to give the story warmth and vigor. One cannot get the more personal details in historical research alone, although I have included bits of history to inform the reader of events surrounding these narratives. If I have succeeded in portraying a more complete picture of this historic family, and let you in on some warm human experiences that few, if any history books contain, I shall have accomplished my purpose.

So, welcome to Eureka and our historic past, and particularly to our greatest Victorian home, the Ingomar, and its distinguished family—the William Carsons.

LET'S TAKE A LOOK AT PAPA

Papa chopping wood and off to work on his familiar bicycle.

The old Methodist Episcopal Church on 3rd & H Streets, Eureka, California.

Papa — The Victorian Gentleman. (overleaf)

et's take a look at the man who inspired these stories. We called him Papa as was customary in the early 1900's. I like to think of him as "The Victorian Gentleman" dressed for a buggy ride with Mama. The buggy rides began when he was courting. In 1904 he rented a "hack" for $2.50, while on his wedding day in 1906, he rented a buggy for $5.00. Papa was very meticulous in his dark suit, starched white shirt and perky bow tie. His brown wavy hair, black moustache and honest brown eyes characterized his pleasing countenance. I never saw him without a moustache.

Dressed for church, he was just as fastidious. The early "church" was not the awe-inspiring Gothic Methodist Sanctuary which he later attended, but a Peniel Mission that had its meeting place in the Metropole Hotel on Second and D streets. It was a family and workingman's hotel, and the mission was located on the ground floor. The hotel still stands. It was here during his "courting days" that he and Mama attended services. Later, as children came into the family, we were taken there to Sunday School. I have very pleasant memories of those early days.

On work days, Papa's role changed to the "Window Washer" when he wore a dark coat and trousers, high laced black shoes, and always a black Pork Pie hat. He rode to work on his high-seated bicycle which in 1903 cost him $16.00. He wore black metal pants guards and carried a galvanized bucket of cleaning materials including coal oil and clean cloths. His bicycle was lighted for night riding by a carbide lamp.

Papa was a small man, but what a capacity for work he had! It was hard work too—not only the window washing which took him to the tops of high buildings including the Humboldt County Court House, but also the floor mopping, dusting, emptying cuspidors in public places, etc. Wood-chopping, pipe-making in his earlier days for the Water Company, ditch-digging, and even cleaning out huge water tanks in a rowboat—these were other jobs he engaged in at various times.

Over a period of seven years, from May 1914 to June 1921, his day book lists approximately 80 buildings, 45 offices, and 170 private homes where he worked, before he devoted most of his time to the Sumner Carson Mansion, The First National Bank, and Green's Garage. His list of Eureka businesses, offices and private homes is a history in itself. So Papa and another well-known caretaker, Mr. Owen Saunderson, helped keep the city's business houses clean.

When I was a child, Papa's day began at 4:30 in the morning. He started his regular work at the First National Bank on the corner of 5th and F in 1911, the year I was born. This accounted for his early rising, so that he could get the bank clean and in order before it opened. He also worked evenings after it closed. Some folks say "banker's hours" are easy. His were not.

Our family adjusted its meals and bedtime to Papa's schedule. Although Papa prepared his own breakfast, our lunch was at noon and supper was on the table at 4:00 p.m. Somehow we managed to be hungry by almost mid-afternoon. We seldom snacked at night. When we did, our snack consisted of crackers and milk, or bread, butter and sugar. Candy, potato chips, pop and gum were either unknown or rarities at best. When Papa brought home a small bag of candy, probably peppermints, it was a special treat.

We had few, if any evenings together as a family. How often I remember my father saying, "Time to get to bed, four-thirty comes pretty early in the morning."

When the working day was finally over, Papa began his preparations for the next day. The ashes in the old green and cream Wedgewood Stove were disposed of after the grate was opened and closed. Then firewood was arranged for the morning fire. The coffee pot was made ready and the table set. Then Papa sat down with his day book and carefully recorded the hours and pay of his day's work—all done in his fancy, neat handwriting. Next, he picked up the Daily Humboldt Standard Newspaper and acquainted himself with the day's events. And finally, he closed his day by reading a chapter from the Bible. This constituted his daily reading. That was all. Mama often said, "I wish Papa would read more." But he seldom did. He needed his rest after a long work day of 8 to 11 hours. I don't remember him ever complaining, but his insistence upon an early bedtime remains very clear.

As a little girl, I often wished that Papa had a more distinguished job. There were times at school when I had to give my father's vocation, and I was embarrassed, although I can't remember anyone ever teasing me about Papa's work. But now when I realize how successful he really was, I am proud of him—and Mama too. For they raised three sons and a daughter: one a Harvard graduate and minister of a large Presbyterian Church in Florida; another, a Stanford graduate, now retired and active in his church; another, a graduate of Humboldt State and a teacher; and the youngest, a successful photographer who studied Aerial Photography during World War II, developed war pictures in the South Pacific as he served in the Navy, and is now a videographer for Channel 6 TV.

But Papa had other roles, too, that are worthy of mention. He took time out from his regular work schedule to keep piles of neatly chopped firewood in the back yard for the cook stove where Mama baked her delicious white bread. He maintained a beautiful garden of roses and rare dahlias from Amelia Carson's imported stock, bordered by a well-trimmed boxwood hedge. He bought leather and tools to half-sole the worn shoes of his active family. And he kept a neat workshop in the back building, that once served as a hay barn, wood shed and shop. He was a collector of nails of all sizes, tools, and parts—each in its own compartment. He threw nothing away.

On Sundays he served as usher with Mr. George

Phraener in the Methodist Church on 3rd and H streets. Mr. Phraener was a much appreciated dry goods man in Daly's Department Store, and advised many a Eureka seamstress on fabrics, patterns, etc. He and Papa made a good pair of ushers. Papa was a member of the Men's Brotherhood Bible Class which met in the large Parsonage next to the church, of the same style of architecture. I was proud of him then. He seemed so distinguished. And as I sat in church with him later sharing his SenSen that he always carried to sweeten his breath, and watched the hands of his big pocket watch go round while the preacher expounded the Scriptures, the hour of the morning service passed slowly. But the heat from the pot-bellied stove kept us warm, and the tones of the large pump organ combined with the beautiful old Methodist hymns, many of which I still remember, all served to create a blessed atmosphere. I still can see the graceful hands of the organist, Mrs. Libbey and I loved to watch her play.

All these years of experience and hard labor culminated in the many years of service to Sumner and Amelia Carson. And that is where our story lies—in Sumner's early years, and later in the mansion built by Sumner in 1914 and lived in by him for nearly 25 years, by Amelia for 43 years, and finally demolished in 1967.

And so the memory and influence of Papa lives on. Humble, yes. Honest and trustworthy—always. Friend of millionaires, indeed! Sumner once said to him, "Mr. Shuster, you are one of my best friends." I'm sure this mutual friendship ripened during the pleasant summer rides in Sumner's Cadillac Roadster, as the two men travelled numerous times to the Carson Bungalow at Maple Creek. There Papa cleaned the mountain retreat, sometimes spending entire days. I think Papa dreamed of the day when he could buy a bungalow for his family. That dream never materialized, but the association with Sumner resulted in a lasting friendship.

A Boy
Named Sumner

◇ 2 ◇

The three-masted schooner *Lottie Carson* was one of the early day sailing fleet of Dolbeer & Carson Lumber Company. She was named after Miss Lottie Carson, daughter of J.M. Carson.

ow to proceed with our story. This young lad, Charles Sumner Carson, will dominate our narrative of the William Carson family—not because he was any more outstanding than his older brother, Milton, his younger sister, Carlotta, or the youngest brother, William Wilson, but because we knew him better due to my father's close association with him in later years. All were born to William and Sarah Carson who had come to Eureka originally from New Brunswick. William Carson left his native land at the age of 24, embarked on the Brazilian, and arrived in San Francisco in April, 1850. At the age of 25 he came to Eureka to engage in the business of lumbering. In a few years of hard labor, good management and great skill, he became what is popularly called "a lumber baron."

Charles Sumner was born in 1873. His unusual name of Sumner may have been taken from the very famous Republican Senator who was deeply opposed to slavery, and fought hard for the freedom of the slaves. He was greatly admired by William Carson. Sumner was not a family name, so the idea seems likely.

Many were the tales William told his children about his hazardous voyage from New Brunswick south to New York, then along the coast of South America, around Cape Horn, northwest to North America, where he finally landed in San Francisco, California. Little did he realize that some day he would be supplying lumber from his own mills in Eureka to build nearly all the Victorian homes of San Francisco's growing metropolis. Nor did he even dream that a very famous architect from that city would be the designer of his own Redwood Castle, that would receive world-wide fame.

I can hear young Sumner asking his father: "Why did you leave your home in New Brunswick to sail all the way to California?"

And his father would reply: "I came in search of gold. Hundreds of people were flocking to California at that time. Then began the period known as "The Gold Rush" and I wanted to be a part of it."

"But how did you happen to change to lumbering?" Sumner would ask.

"I guess I had it in my blood. I believed I could make more money cutting down the huge redwood trees I saw growing in great abundance, and make lumber for fine homes. And so I found a partner, John Dolbeer, and we began our work together.

Also when I was quite young, I helped my father, an immigrant from Northern Ireland, stockpile lumber for freighters. Yes, I had the feel of lumber in my blood—and it was good!"

Sumner may have traced the route his father had taken on his father's large globe of the world in his private office and retreat. The room contained a sizeable roll-top desk, a built-in glass case of stuffed game birds, and an open fireplace. There stood the world globe on which his father often followed the routes of his numerous sailing ships, and of personal trips he made to foreign lands. And as Sumner noted the mileage and the lines of travel on the map, he was astounded. His father had made the long trip safely on treacherous oceans, through fair and stormy weather in seven long months.

No doubt Sumner was challenged by many ideas as he listened to his father's adventures. Would he sail the high seas for excitement? Would he seek for gold, or be a lumberman like his father or grandfather? It would be very hard to make a decision.

THE MANSION —
FLAMBOYANT THEN,
ELEGANT NOW

3

Earliest picture of Carson Mansion, with the red and white striped roof. Note the Cookhouse located behind Carriage House.

Newspaper drawing of the construction. (overleaf)

hen Sumner was eleven years old, Milton, nineteen, Carlotta seventeen, and William Jr. seven—their father made a tremendous decision. Business was dropping off because of the great depression. There was an unexpected decrease in the foreign demand for lumber, and an overproduction from too many mills. Carson was worried that he wouldn't continue to have enough work for all the men he employed. And then he remembered "his dream" to build a great mansion. He told his family:

"It will be the most wonderful home you have ever seen! It will be a castle of redwood, and so beautiful that people from all over the world will come to see it. And you will live in it! We shall build a tower so high that we can see all over Humboldt Bay. We shall watch our ships, loaded with lumber, sail away to distant lands. We shall see the sun rise and set. And you may climb the stairway to the very top every day and see the spectacular view, just as I intend to do."

"I shall begin at once," he said, "and I shall continue to hire all my millworkers so that not one of them will be out of work. There will be more than a hundred carpenters, plumbers, famous woodcarvers and other craftsmen. And I shall send my ships to foreign countries to buy many kinds of beautiful wood for the interior of our home. The foundation will be two feet thick so that no earthquake, however strong, can shake it down. It will endure for centuries."

And so the castle was begun. Exactly when, is not definitely known because of the scarcity of newspaper publicity. I searched micro-film newspapers published during the building years and found only brief comments. On July 26, 1884, the Humboldt Standard stated: "Carson's residence has been commenced." The Times Telephone of that same date announced, "The work of laying the foundation of Mr. Carson's new dwelling is fast approaching completion." There seems to have been no picture of the actual construction, no account of its final completion, and no news of any housewarming festivities. However, on Oct. 6, 1884, the Standard made this observation: "The tower of Mr. Carson's new residence looms up from the lower end of Second Street."

Much has been written describing the architecture of the Carson Mansion. Benjamin Sacks in his book "Carson Mansion and Ingomar Theater" gives a most detailed account of both exterior and interior design along with beautiful photos. Our purpose, as given in the preface, is to focus on family life inside the mansion, so we shall leave the architectural details to other writers. A few interesting observations are in order.

The home was constructed on an entire block, while the yard and carriage house were a part of a two block area. Children and adults watched in wonder as the Redwood Castle with its 68 foot tower; its eight gables, no one like any other; its basement and three stories with 18 rooms, surrounded by spacious balconies and porches—all reached toward the sky.

Carson insisted that the framing and exterior be entirely of redwood; while the interior wood consisting of the finest grade of seasoned redwood, oak, mahogany from Central and South America, teak from the Orient, and 97,000 feet of primavera from South America, has been called its "crowning glory."

Elaborate stained glass windows, bevelled mirrors from England, French dining room tapestry, Mexican onyx fireplaces, and intricate woodcarving by Irish, Swiss and possibly Italian artisans, all added to the interior beauty of the home such as had never before been seen in the small lumbering town of Eureka.

Even though it was a time of depression, redwood lumber was abundant and reasonable. A most interesting observation on building activity at this time appeared in the Humboldt Standard on July 29, 1884. It read as follows:

"Rapid growth is manifested in every portion of the city. The forests of timber are being rapidly merged into forests of chimneys, and handsome dwellings are being erected upon the places where but a few short years ago we went blackberrying, or rested upon a fallen tree and gazed back upon the distant town. The place known as Pine's Pasture, which until recently was a first class dairy ranch, has lost every distinctive feature, and at present is as much a part of the city as Clark's Addition or any other suburban locality, and the sound of the hammer and saw is heard constantly in that direction."

This was the kind of community the Redwood Mansion became a part of—tall redwood trees surrounding the city; an unpaved 2nd Street with its weekend revelries as woodsmen and sailors swarmed into town; 43 new homes and buildings being erected in 1884; whole blocks being purchased by Captain Buhne, Thomas Baird, Major Long and F.A. Weck with buildings being erected for business purposes; churches entering the area and becoming a very vital part of community life; and a "flamboyant" mansion, painted in some kind of green or dark color, and "flaunting" a red and white striped roof, rising in the midst.

That description does not characterize the grand, stately Ingomar of today—flamboyant then; elegant now.

The actual date of the Carson move into the Mansion is not definitely known. Some have set it in Oct. 1886. It presumably took some little adjustment for Sarah Bell Carson to leave her more humble home where she did her own housekeeping, cooking, baking and gardening, to enter the stately mansion as the "Baron's Lady," and to turn over her house and yard duties to servants, cooks and gardeners. But as she and her family became established in their new residence, described by Wm. Pierson as "unadulterated joy," she no doubt became accustomed and thrilled with her prominent role. A look at the old dwelling, now located at 1521 3rd, and a drive up 2nd Street to the stately mansion will help anyone capture the tremendous emotion that must have been shared by the entire family as they entered their fabulous home. (My grandson Gary Lane would have described it as "awesome"!)

Historical Note:

The original location of the old home was 130 "M" Street, while the new location to which it has been moved is 1521 3rd. It was constructed in 1871 by Dan Pickert, a bookkeeper at the mill, but vacated on the death of his wife, and sold to William Carson in 1872. The two-story historical home was purchased in April 1982 by Bob and Agnes Sobrito who have converted it into the beautiful "Old Town Bed and Breakfast Inn." All newly carpeted and renovated, it retains the Victorian style and is fitted with lovely antique furniture. You will enjoy the hospitality of the Sobritos. They are delighted with the history of the residence, and will share that joy with their guests.

Original home of William and Sarah Carson — now the Old Town Bed & Breakfast Inn at 1521 Third Street, Eureka, California.

"Gingerbread"

4

The Carson house or "Pink Lady" was built as a wedding gift for Milton Carson and his bride in 1889.

The "Pink Lady" adorned in all her "gingerbread." (overleaf)

was recently intrigued with the word "gingerbread." For many years I had accepted the term as a description of the lavish wood decorations on our old Victorian homes. I had grown up with these homes all about me—very large, unpainted or rather, paint-worn residences with no particular beauty. Having lived in a smaller Victorian for about twenty years, I was familiar with the high ceilings, dark woodwork, and lack of some modern conveniences. I was not impressed. Twenty-five years ago when my mother-in-law from the San Diego area suggested that the Victorian homes in Eureka should be repainted (she was a quarter of a century in advance of her time) I immediately protested. Hadn't they always been drab and color-less—at least in my generation?

And then it happened! A new surge of interest in Victorian homes took place, and people began restoring and repainting the long neglected gingerbread structures. Painting became an art indeed when the ornate decorations were skillfully repainted to accentuate the intricate designs. A few home owners seeking to emphasize the gingerbread came out with a shocking combination of contrasting colors, so unlike the original intention. But on the whole, Eureka began to take on a grand new look and homes that had deteriorated for years now became much sought after dwellings.

I read with interest that our good friend Robert Madsen, one-time mayor of our city, now deceased, received "the first Certificate of Merit Award for the restoration and preservation of a Victorian home." In 1963 he purchased the mansion across the street from the Carson Mansion, and began some restoration and refurbishing which resulted in the beautiful "Pink Lady" now standing.

This beautiful home with its superb stained glass windows in the front porch rotunda, its stately round turret on the right hand corner, fish scale shingles on the outside frame, and a good share of gingerbread to enhance the dignified exterior, stands as a classic example of a true Victorian dwelling. It was designed by a Newsome architect and given by William Carson to his oldest son, John Milton, as a wedding present in 1889. Milton lived in the home until the death of his father in 1912, after which he moved back into the mansion across the street.

"Gingerbread"—where did the name originate? It first referred to fancy ginger-flavored English cakes. Later, sailing vessels began ornamenting their exteriors with carved and gilded decorations, and they were called gingerbread motifs. And finally, the word was extended to the very fancy and ornate wood decorations on large Victorian homes built in the late 1800's.

To describe the gingerbread adorning the Carson Mansion is beyond the ability of the average layman. How does one explain a "fairyland of architectural wonderment"? I shall not try. When one approaches the Redwood Castle and views it in all of its extravagant beauty, gingerbread becomes a most sophisticated word for such an elaborate array of extremely beautiful decoration. It defies description. But it is there to behold in all of its captivating charm and preserved beauty.

The Gingerbread Mansion in Ferndale, California, located at 400 Berding Street is a classic example of gingerbread art. As one views the almost fragile-looking carved woodwork, he is made to wonder at its enduring quality. The mansion, which has been featured in several national magazines, is one of the most photographed buildings in Humboldt County. It was originally the home of Dr. Ring, local Ferndale physician, and is now a Bed and Breakfast establishment. Ferndale, located just 17 miles south of Eureka, has its ample share of unusual gingerbread homes, and has been appropriately named "The Victorian Village."

To be more practical and down-to-earth, gingerbread has also been defined as "the offspring of the industrial age." After the Civil War, machines—particularly lathes—that had produced materials for the Union Army, now turned wooden siding into fancy scrolls, grill work, and carved or engraved articles sometimes also called "scrimshaw." Then as neighbor tried to outdo neighbor in adorning his home with these unusual decorations, the wooden motifs became a symbol of wealth and prosperity. Surely the Carson home reached the pinnacle of this status symbol.

The Gingerbread Mansion — 400 Berding Street Ferndale, California; today the Gingerbread Mansion Bed and Breakfast.

Eureka terminus of the Eel River and Eureka Railroad.

Alton depot.

THE YEAR 1885, WHEN SUMNER WAS TWELVE

The old Humboldt County Courthouse on 5th and J Streets, Eureka, California. Built in 1885 at a cost of $166,622.10.

he year 1885 must have been a memorable year for young Sumner. Besides the building of his father's Redwood Castle begun in 1884, which produced much more excitement than one twelve year old could contain, there were other outstanding events. Although the Carson family prospered, 1885 was a year of depression, and the small town of Eureka suffered exceedingly. It is said that people walked the streets begging for food. A Welfare Committee was appointed to provide food and shelter for the needy, and William Carson became a member.

But it was also a year of greater building. The cornerstone for the new Humboldt County Court House was laid by the Masonic Lodge on July 4, and the first bricks were laid on May 29, 1885.

The need for a new Court House was great. An interesting and humorous story appeared in the local newspaper on Dec. 7, 1883 entitled "Our Court House." It read as follows:

"What is that rickety old building over there?" inquires the stranger with no little awe in his voice and manner, like one who is gazing for the first time upon an Egyptian mummy or the tomb of forgotten kings. "That building," answers his companion, "Oh, that's our Court House."

"Yes?" in a surprised tone, "and what are those bars in the windows above for?"

"Those barred windows? Why that's our jail."

"You don't say!" And the stranger endeavors to conceal

his derision and contempt while in the company of those who are courteously showing him about the city.

"Seriously, our Court House is a disgrace to the city and county," states the newspaper.

This article must have had its effect. For in 1885 it was decided to build a bigger and better County building, and the Supervisors suggested that it be built on the City Plaza. At that time, the Plaza, bounded by 4th and 5th and "I" and "J" streets, was a very important center of community activity, especially on the Fourth of July, when there were great celebrations there. Picnics, fireworks, and sporting events were popular.

It is interesting to note that the original lot was purchased for $100, and at one time it was fenced and used as a pasture. Now it would be the center of County activity. It is also interesting to discover that Eureka has been the County seat since 1856.

The construction of the new Court House is exciting to read about. How thrilling would it have been for young Sumner to leave the building of his father's mansion and travel the short distance to the Court House site and watch its progress also. The Court House was framed with steel and brick. It has been estimated that one million bricks were used. In order to supply them, John Duprey opened a brick yard in the gulch west of the Myrtle Grove Cemetery. No doubt the hauling of the bricks from there to the building site was of immense interest to the youth of that day.

Not only was brick used in great quantities, but also sand and gravel furnished by Wm. Newell. Seven hundred tons of Mad River gravel were transported on barges through the canal into Humboldt Bay, and thence to Eureka. Sand for the concrete came from Samoa Peninsula at 5¢ per ton.

The iron work was furnished by Biglow and Little of San Francisco, and the stone by Carlaw Bros. of Sacramento.

The Court House was constructed in four sections and was officially occupied in Jan. 1889. The total cost of the building was $166,622.10. Just for comparison, the Mansion is estimated to have cost $90,000.00, but is valued at 3 million on today's market. In 1893 a huge Seth Thomas clock, 9 feet in diameter, was installed in the Court House Tower. In May of that year it was ordered to have the clock strike regularly throughout the entire twenty-four hours.

With all of this fine construction—brick, stone, cement and steel—the building did not survive, while the mansion of redwood did. In 1950 the tower had to be removed for safety reasons, and in 1954 (December of) a very destructive earthquake left the grand old court house unsafe for future use. It was vacated and demolished.

Again, Papa comes into the picture, but not until 29 years later. The Court House had 71 windows, and Papa began washing them in 1914. It took him two days to wash all of them, at 15¢ a window—a grand total of $10.65 for two days of hard work. He was 43 years of age, and had been married only 8 years. He had a very full work schedule. His popularity as an efficient and thorough window washer was spreading. And though it was hard work, and his hands were almost constantly in water, he never forgot his evening ritual of rose-water and glycerin to prevent his hands from becoming rough and worn. As usual, he was very meticulous.

Yet another event of monumental historical interest was the expulsion of Chinese from Eureka and vicinity in that same year. "Hang every Chinaman, and burn Chinatown to the last stick." This was the cry of an angry mob of citizens who gathered on First Street following the accidental shooting of Mr. Kendall, a Eureka city councilman. He had heard the noises of violence on the north side of 4th Street and had gone to investigate. Tong wars had become prevalent, due to two factions in the Chinese Community whose headquarters centered on 4th and E Streets. About 200 men were divided between the groups known as the Masons and the Highbinders. They were well-armed with "bulldog revolvers, cleaverlike knives, and ugly iron bars." And so, although the fighting was confined to the Chinese quarters, stray bullets sometimes escaped—once hitting a little white boy in the foot, and now a city councilman who succumbed to the shot.

The Chinese who settled here in the mid 1870's were often abused by their white neighbors. Young people made sport of the Chinese and molested them without cause. A very disgraceful incident took place on First Street by a mob who threw rocks into Chinese windows during a New Year's celebration, breaking sashes and windows, demolishing doors, and even hitting the celebrants inside. And another affair in Rohnerville was a deliberate murder by a white man of a Chinese laundryman who only demanded money that was due him. His skull was crushed by a hard blow.

The Chinese had been in the area for about twelve years. Some had come to find gold, some worked on the railroads, and others in the mines in eastern Humboldt. However, as they settled in Eureka, they began establishing businesses of their own, including laundries, produce stands, and serving as domestic or yard men in prominent Eureka homes.

But the prejudice against them aroused hatred and rebellion especially when shots intended for their own people went out of bounds. The Chinese community occupied the worst section of Eureka and had been described as a "festering sinkhole of vice."

And so on Feb. 6, 1885 the crowds gathered shouting their cries of revenge for the shooting of David Kendall. Before the cries broke forth into violence, a town meeting was called in the Centennial Hall. Three leading men of both Chinese groups were brought in and given the stern command that all Chinamen in the area must be ready to depart in 24 hours. The Chinese were quick to respond, and in less than 48 hours they were ready. Some were brought in from ranch and lumber camp cookhouses, etc. They all gathered in warehouses waiting to sail away to San Francisco in two steamships—the Humboldt and the Chester. There were over 300 men and from 20 to 30 women ready to board the ships. Two of the men were seriously wounded. One hundred and fifty tons of cargo were loaded on board. The City Marshall of Eureka accompanied this unusual shipment of unwanted Chinese and their belongings. Evidently no word had been sent ahead of their coming, but the city officials said their presence would make little difference in San Francisco's large Chinese population.

Whether young Sumner was at home at the time, or attending school in San Francisco, we do not know. If he were in Eureka, he might have been on the scene at daylight to see the great activity taking place on 4th Street, as express wagons, drays and other transportation facilities of all kinds were employed to carry the loads of belongings down to the bay. Twenty-three deliveries were reported at the wharf before noon. Crowds of people gathered to watch this unusual exodus. Although good order prevailed and there was no violence, one incident occurred which was uncalled for. A scaffold was erected on 4th between E and F Streets, with all the hanging paraphernalia at hand. It was totally unnecessary, but indicated the strong feelings of hatred that existed.

And yet another outstanding event occurred in that memorable year. The introduction of the electric light into Eureka was accompanied by great excitement and much pleasure. On the evening of Oct. 22, 1885, Second Street in the vicinity of the Vance Hotel was suddenly aglow with lights "almost as bright as if old Sol had not gone to rest below the horizon."

Appropriately, large crowds turned out to view the miracle, which had been awaited for some time. John Vance, responsible for many of Eureka's improvements, was given the credit for the city's first electric light. He had planned to inaugurate the occasion on a small scale, but the demand became so great before the insulators were placed in position, that he was forced to send for a generator nearly four times as large as the one originally ordered. It arrived on the steamer Humboldt on Sunday, and was soon placed in position. At 6:00 p.m., just a few days after its arrival, the electric machine in Vance's Mill was started. Although a little irregular at first, it was soon regulated as the crowd watched breathlessly. Would the new venture be a success? Soon eight lights glowed in five separate locations—one in front of the Vance Hotel; one in Cohn and Co.'s Liquor Store; two in Crocker Bros. Store; three in Vance's Mill, and one at Vance's Wharf.

Second Street would soon take on a "decidedly handsome appearance." However, F Street had also "caught the fever," and it too would soon be brilliantly lighted.

And finally, the entry into Eureka of the Eel River and Eureka Railroad, completed the series of events which characterized that very special year of 1885. One thousand people were on hand to witness the first excursion over this railroad that virtually inaugurated the opening of the first train passage out of Eureka. It took place in July 1885 under the auspices of the Excelsior Lyceum of Eureka. The terminus was 22 miles south of Eureka, and two miles east of Alton. It was named Burnell's after Joe Burnell, from whom the depot site was purchased. At that time, the town of Hydesville was just 2 miles away. Stage coaches and freight wagons frequented the busy town. Burnell's consisted of a passenger depot, a large freight house, a small locomotive house, and a turntable.

No doubt young Sumner looked forward to the day when the railroad would run all the way through to San Francisco. As of now, the big metropolitan area could only be reached by boat, and it sometimes took several days—especially if rough waters were encountered.

In the year 1984 we think we are living in a most exciting age. But we are so accustomed to amazing inventions that sometimes we accept them with much less enthusiasm than the early citizens of Eureka, when electric lights literally transformed their night hours, while the short railroad of 22 miles was as exciting as the automobile taking the place of carriages.

And so the year 1885 saw Eureka well on the road to progress.

THE WOOD-BURNING FURNACE

A side entrance of the Carson Mansion with "Engineer" Arthur Baldwin and son Edmund, 1931.

hen William Carson built his mansion, he had an abundance of redwood from his mills to provide burning material for a furnace that would send heat throughout the entire house. And so he had a large furnace installed in the basement. As the fire burned, a boiler of water was heated, which water was then transported in pipes to radiators in nearly every room of the house. When the water cooled, it returned to the boiler to be reheated, so there was a continuous circulation.

I have never read anything on this subject, but I have interviewed a native Eurekan, Ed Baldwin, whose father, Arthur Baldwin was head caretaker or "engineer" of the mansion for thirty-three years. Ed has a first-hand knowledge of the heating operation, having accompanied his dad many times to his work. Arthur Baldwin, a second cousin to William Carson, took over this job in 1905. When Ed was six years old, he remembers how his dad sometimes arose at four in the morning to get the big furnace going. This happened on cold frosty mornings, or perhaps on extremely damp, foggy days.

Now, keeping the fire burning was no easy task. Stored away in the drying area of the basement were stacks of wood that had been previously handled many times before the wood was ready for burning. It had been hauled from the mill to the back yard of the mansion by Mr. Buck (R.L.) Hanson, a well-known man in the wood business, who sold and delivered wood to many Eurekans for their cooking and heating stoves.

The wood was stacked in the yard in large quantities. It consisted of slash and trim, soaking wet, from Carson's sawmill, and was very heavy to handle. It was later carried in a two-wheel cart to the basement, where it was transferred to the drying area. "This," says Ed, "was a relentless job."

When Mr. Baldwin was ready to build a fire, he could go to the drying area and get wood that was ready to burn. He would start the fire and begin heating the water in the boiler. And, as the water heated and rose through the pipes to the radiators, the mansion began to warm up and be comfortable. All day long the fire was kept burning. In between times of stoking the furnace, Mr. Baldwin prepared more wood, cutting long pieces 4 or 5 ft. in length into smaller ones that would fit inside the furnace. It took the greater part of his time preparing the wood.

Arthur Baldwin kept the Carson Mansion warm for thirty-three years, and then retired due to ill health. Three years later he died. After he left, an oil burner was installed to heat the boiler, and the strenuous days of stoking wood were over. At the time of this writing (1983) the furnace has been converted to gas.

When Sumner Carson built his mansion on 6th and "J", he too had a wood furnace installed. When I interviewed Roy Tanner, after the mansion was demolished, he told me the furnace burned twenty-five cords of wood a year. And another twenty-five cords were stored in the wood shed for the coming year. I expect the same system of heating was used here.

I learned from Roy Tanner that my father cleaned the chimney flue when he was alive, and later Roy took over. But somehow, when I saw the clouds of black dust and soot emerge from the inside of the roof on that cold, eerie day of destruction when the attic was exposed, and high walls were being battered down, I knew it must be an accumulation of soot over a period of many years. Now, as I reflect, that chimney may not have been cleaned during those later years when Amelia Carson lived alone, except for her housekeeper, and found the furnace room a retreat from the beautiful upstairs mansion she had once enjoyed. Her walking days were nearly over, and her life revolved around her large brown leather chair in front of the furnace, her basement apartment once occupied by a Philippino cook, and her family of cats tended by faithful "Gussie" who carefully prepared and fed them their very special meals.

As hundreds and thousands of tourists pass by the immaculately preserved William Carson mansion, now the Ingomar Club, it seems that very little has changed. But as I drive by the modern and beautiful Times Standard building, situated where the Sumner mansion once stood, I recall a passerby on that second day of destruction saying, "Isn't it sad? I think they should have kept it for a museum or something." And in my mind's eye I see radiators being thrown from second story windows—radiators that had once been installed to warm the mansion that is no more. And I remember the "old wood furnace" with a fire burning brightly, a boiler full of heated water, and mansions cozy and comfortable on cold foggy days. Yes, "the old wood furnace"—which is what this story is all about had a very important function in the earlier days when wood abounded. Many of us have returned to the warmth and comfort of a wood-burning stove.

View of the Mill with the Courthouse Tower and Carson Mansion in the background.

Dolbeer and Carson Lumber Company's "Bay Mill", Eureka.

Sumner and His Brothers In The Mill

7

Sumner Carson in Alaska during The Gold Rush.

Aerial view of the Dolbeer Carson Mill by Merle Shuster taken in 1947. (overleaf)

n the year 1890 when Sumner was only seventeen years old, he decided to join the "gold rush" to Alaska. His father had made his own decision forty years earlier, but had afterward concluded that there was more gold in the redwoods. But young Sumner had to see for himself. Gold had been discovered in the Juneau region ten years earlier, but unbeknown to Sumner, the best finds were yet to come. No doubt his parents warned him of the temptations to which he would be exposed in the rough mining camps—the very kind of influence they had shielded him from in the lumbering haunts of his own locality. A picture of the adventurous gold miner in the San Francisco Chronicle shows him in a fur parka with hood over his head, so that only his eager face with dark eyes, heavy dark eyebrows and moustache is showing. No known stories of his Alaskan experiences have been recorded—only to say that Sumner returned home and joined his father in the lumbering operations. Mrs. Sterling Avery formerly of San Francisco, and niece of the Carsons, has some nuggets and other mementos that Sumner brought home from his Alaskan trip.

When our returned prospector walked into the Bay Mill near his mansion home he was struck with the system and order which prevailed. He could see that it was not by chance that his father had achieved such success, but by excellent management of the entire premises. He realized that if he were to have a part in the operation, he would have to adopt such methods also. He was aware that his brothers Milton and William would also seek a share in the business. And so young Sumner determined to work hard, learn all he could, and earn his right to become an active partner.

The three boys all became experienced lumber men and assumed positions of responsibility, so that when their father died in 1912 they were able to take over his huge operation. In fact, two years before his death, Carson placed the active management of his business into their hands. John Milton, the oldest, became president and assumed general responsibility for production in Eureka; while William Wilson, who had assumed the duties of John Dolbeer, Carson's partner, in San Francisco when Dolbeer died in 1902, continued to head the sales office there.

Dolbeer and Carson had been partners for thirty-seven years and to Dolbeer with his inventive mind goes the credit for the invention of the steam donkey used to haul huge redwood logs to the open trails. This invention had revolutionized the logging business. At the time of Dolbeer's death he and Carson owned 20,000 acres of the finest redwoods in the world. Their Bay Mill had a capacity of 70,000 ft. daily. And as new equipment appeared they kept pace with the circular saw, bandsaw and turning lathe. At the time Sumner left for Alaska they owned three shingle mills which produced a total of 130,000 shingles daily. I'm sure we still see some of those "ornate" shingles on old Victorian homes here in Eureka. They also had interest in railroads, lumber schooners and vessels, and part interest in other lumber companies and mills, and oil land acreage.

When William Carson died he was a multimillionaire. What a contrast to the young man who had arrived in Eureka in 1850 when the little community was only one month old and had a population of 200. The area of Humboldt had been described as a "trackless wilderness where men had discovered the greatest stand of timber on earth." Just thirty-three years later, in an article from the Philadelphia Press, it was estimated that with redwood lumber at $18 per 1000 feet, the forests of Humboldt County would pay the national debt of the United States. But lumber was greatly needed for building, particularly in San Francisco where it was said that San

Francisco was building as never a city had built before.

It is time to get a more complete picture of the three Carson sons. John Milton was 47 years old when he assumed management of the Dolbeer Carson Co. and continued for 29 years. He was known as the Dean of Redwood Manufacturers throughout the West. He has been described as a kind, gallant man, friendly and cooperative. In 1924, twelve years after his father's death, he supervised the building of a modern electric mill, which was another "first" in our redwood area. It has been observed that although his father had been very proud of the Bay Mill which he and Dolbeer had constructed in 1875, he no doubt would have approved of the "complete junking" of this plant for the new modern one. This latter mill continued in operation under the Carsons until 1950 when it was purchased by the Pacific Lumber Company. The seventy-five successful years of Carson ownership had come to an end.

An interesting observation of Milton's personality was his love for the outdoors. Not only was he an authority on fish and their propogation, but he was also an avid bird watcher. It was not uncommon for him to interrupt a business conference to call attention to a flock of birds migrating to our Humboldt Coast. His office window overlooking the Bay afforded him an excellent view of the seabirds he enjoyed so much.

While living in the Mansion after his father's death, Milton also owned a fishing lodge at Klamath Glen, and a hunting lodge in Fieldbrook. His beautiful Victorian home, now known as the Pink Lady, a wedding gift to him and his wife Mary Bell from his father in 1889, was leased and sold the year Milton moved into the Mansion. And in 1937 Milton and Mary Bell celebrated their golden wedding anniversary in the elegant home they had enjoyed for twenty-five years. It was a gala event with an informal open house both afternoon and evening.

In later years, Milton was in poor health due to a heart problem, but continued to work in his office across the street almost to the end.

John Milton's youngest brother, William Junior, became vice-president of the Mill in 1912 and remained so until his death in 1937 when he was only sixty years old. William grew

41

up in Eureka but later moved to San Francisco where he lived for forty years, and assumed Dolbeer's duties in 1902. He continued to head the sales office there until he died. William never married.

Each of the boys left a large fortune, but William's is significant in the fact that he left much to his boyhood friends in "Pines Pasture" who later worked in the Carson Mill. Many of us local Eurekans are familiar with the name, but not so sure where the Pasture was located. We found a description in the Humboldt Historian which fixes the boundaries from Carson's Cookhouse, then located behind the Carriage House, to Tannery Gulch; and from what is now Stanton's Restaurant on 5th to the Eureka Slough area. The pasture was a small subdivision, owned by Safford Pine, who was also owner of the Acme Foundry. Although he kept cattle on the land, he evidently didn't object to boys having lots of good times there. Arden Scott tells of the fun he and his brother Bud had in Pine's Pasture jumping from piling to the soft mud flats. They lived in the vicinity of Third and W.

Not only did William remember his boyhood friends, but, he like his father, left a liberal bequest to Christ Church and to numerous charitable institutions. Also to hospitals and to employees of companies in which he was interested. Two outstanding donations were made to our city—one of $50,000 for the Carson Memorial, located on Harris and J. This building, now used for many social and civic events, was built as a memorial to his father and displays a picture of both father and son. Much of the money for Carson Park, a children's playground at Carson and H, occupying two full blocks, came from William's estate. It seems that more publicity has been given to the will of William Wilson than to those of the other two boys.

A word about Carlotta, the second child of William Sr. is in order. She married Robert James Tyson, a San Francisco insurance broker, and lived in the Piedmont district of Oakland in an impressive Mediterranean style residence of three stories. The marriage ended in a divorce in 1914. Carlotta was described in the Times newspaper as "one of the wealthiest women in the west." She died in San Francisco in 1932.

The Carson Mansion was last occupied by the Clarence

42

La Boyteaux family. Sara Bell Carson, daughter of John Milton, married Mr. La Boyteaux of Fort Bragg who eventually became the superintendent of logging for Dolbeer and Carson. They sold the residence occupied by family members for sixty-five years to a group of Eureka businessmen, (as noted elsewhere in our stories) now incorporated into the Ingomar Club.

And thus the Carson regime in Eureka ended. It covered a period of one hundred years. William arrived in Eureka in 1850 and the Dolbeer Carson Mill was acquired by the Pacific Lumber Co. in 1950. It was an era of great prosperity including elegant mansions, enormous wealth, relaxing summer homes, fishing and hunting lodges, tremendous investments, huge holdings, and enviable inheritances; consummating in wills to relatives, employees, universities, hospitals, churches, and the city of Eureka—and even to Amelia's cats!

Papa would have had his sights on "another mansion" where there would be no windows to wash, floors to scrub or carved woodwork to polish. And he would have shared his deep religious faith with his millionaire friends, particularly with his good friend Sumner. Maybe that was the reason Sumner appreciated him so much.

Aerial view of Carson Mill.

The Mill's power and fuel house.

Interior view of the "Bay Mill", showing a typical mill scene.

SUMNER'S WEDDING

The sailing vessel "North Fork" on which Sumner and Amelia embarked on their honeymoon.   Wallace E. Martin collection

he was "one of Eureka's fairest daughters, highly accomplished in social and musical circles." Her name was Amelia Emily Ohman, a native daughter of Eureka, who was soon to be the bride of a native son, Charles Sumner Carson. The event was to take place on Jan. 1, 1900.

Sumner was now twenty-seven years old and ready to settle down in a home of his own. It would not be as pretentious as his family home, but it was described as an "imposing residence at the head of 4th Street." Sumner had purchased it from the Boyd family and "refurbished it for his bride."

The wedding day arrived, and the Ohman home, located on 4th and "I" was beautifully decorated for the occasion. "Festoons of evergreen and a profusion of rare potted plants and cut flowers" adorned the parlors and dining room. "Avenues of palms with interlacing festoons of evergreens" beautified the hallways, staircase and vestibule. Thus it was described in eloquent newspaper language.

It was a private occasion with only family members present, and two close friends, Julia Gall and her sister, Mrs. J. Vansant, Jr. The parents of both bride and groom were present, along with fourteen close relatives, including brothers Milton and William.

As the Carson family approached the Ohman home in their handsome carriages, it was still early morning. The wedding was scheduled for 8:00 a.m., to be followed by an elaborate wedding breakfast in the spacious dining room, in the warmth and glow of the fireplace. Lighted Tiffany lamps would add to the beauty of the occasion.

William Sr.'s carriage approached the Ohman residence at a slow measured gait, drawn by a pacer horse. It was a beautiful Phaeton-style rig in dark Brewster green, with pale green striping on the springs. The dashboard and fenders were covered with patent leather so that the mud and dust from the streets would not adhere to them. In case of rain, it had a covered top, and in the darkness could be lit by two impressive lights, one on each side of the seat.

But Sumner's thoughts no doubt travelled far ahead of the slow-moving carriage to the home where he would behold his lovely bride in her wedding gown. And he would stand beside her, as the rector of Christ Episcopal Church, Rev. Caleb Benham, would pronounce them man and wife.

Guests and family were arriving as the carriage drew up, and the horse was secured to the iron hitching post. And as the fog began to clear and the sky brightened, Sumner knew it would be a perfect day.

As Sumner entered and was soon to stand beneath the floral arrangement described as "a true lover's knot of white chrysanthemums and pink rosebuds" his joy knew no bounds. Standing with him would be Rudolph Ohman, the bride's brother. Soon the two men took their places as the music began. Julie Gall, the bridesmaid, approached the wedding party. She was dressed in white silk trimmed in light blue and carried a bouquet of azaleas and carnations tied in blue ribbon. Suddenly all eyes were upon the festooned stairway as the beautiful bride descended in her white silk pearl-trimmed gown with a lace yoke, and wearing diamond jewelry. Her train or veil was finger tip, in those days called a demitrain. Carrying a bouquet of white roses and maiden-hair fern with white taffeta ribbon, she slowly approached the waiting group, and found her place beside the groom. And then the short ceremony which would "launch the lovers on a new life for a New Year" was performed, and Sumner kissed his lovely wife.

Good wishes and congratulations were in order as the happy couple proceeded to the dining room for breakfast. Seated around the wedding table were all the twenty family members and friends. But they could not linger long, for a trip to San Francisco was scheduled beginning at 10:30 at the Fields Landing boat dock. The bride must change to her tailor-made travelling suit of blue Venetian fabric, and be ready to leave in a carriage for the Eel River and Eureka railroad where they would board a train for the little town of Fields Landing, some five miles to the south. We smile as we think of a train ride to Fields Landing, but it was the fastest means of transportation and the boat would embark early. The steamer North Fork was waiting when they arrived. The newlyweds boarded the ship amidst the farewells and good wishes of their loved ones and began the ocean voyage to San Francisco, the big metropolis, the city that everyone admired.

Many "old-timers" considered the trip a pleasure cruise of 18-20 hours. The accommodations were excellent and included immaculate sleeping quarters and delicious meals. And like a modern plane with its stewardess, the vessel provided the services of a pleasant woman, dressed in a neat blue and white uniform, to care for the needs of women and children.

As the ship passed through the treacherous bar which was often rough and dangerous, and reached calmer waters, Amelia and Sumner breathed easier, and settled down to enjoy their honeymoon—alone at last on the sunlit waters of the blue Pacific.

A drawing of The William Carson Phaeton Carriage.

49

A Sad Windy Day

9

An aerial view of the Carson Mansion, its out buildings and gardens showing their proximity to the Mill.

here was a cold wind blowing in Eureka, California on the day of Feb. 19, 1912, significant of the sadness that hung over the city. William Carson, beloved millionaire, mill owner, employer, and generous benefactor was dead. He died in his redwood castle at 3:15 p.m. after a 4 months illness, to which he succumbed. Dr. H.G. Gross, his physician, had told the members of his family at the beginning of the illness, which was pneumonia, to expect the end speedily. "But the physician seemed to have overlooked that constitution that was responsible for the erect form and firm step which at 87 years of age and up to the time of his illness, made William Carson so conspicuous a figure as he walked from his home, down town and back again." So read the Humboldt Standard on Feb. 20. The article was headlined, "William Carson Has Passed to the Great Beyond." "The vitality of the man was wonderful," it stated. "For the past four weeks not a particle of nourishment had entered his body, yet he lived on and was conscious up to a few days ago."

Carson's three sons, Milton, Sumner and William were with him at the time of his death. His one daughter, Carlotta of Piedmont, Ca., was unable to attend because of illness. His wife Sarah, had passed away in 1904.

Thus ended a life of 87 years, 62 of which had been spent in the small but growing town of Eureka of which he had been a most vital part, and in which he had amassed his great fortune.

53

As the word of Carson's death reached the downtown and mill areas about 4:00 p.m., little groups gathered on street corners and passed the news from one Eurekan to another. Conversations among mill-workers may have sounded like the following:

"Have you heard the sad news?" asked one. "Our boss is dead. Will the mills continue to operate, and will we still have our jobs?"

"Oh yes," replied the other. "As you know, for the past two years, the sons have taken over. Milton will be a fine manager, and is well-trained in his father's methods. There is no need to worry."

"Do you remember the wonderful gifts he gave us at Christmas time?" said another. "The money always came in handy for our children's presents."

"Yes," was the reply. "And the turkeys we always received on Thanksgiving and Christmas. I remember one Christmas when we were really up against it, a huge grocery wagon loaded with supplies, stopped at our door and furnished us with food for many days. This happened to many families, and will never be forgotten."

"How long have you been working at Dolbeer and Carson's mill?"

"I have been there for twenty years, and I know others who have worked there thirty and forty."

"Do you remember the hard times of 1893 when every mill in the county was forced to close, and men were out of work by the hundreds?"

"Yes, I will never forget—every mill but Carson's. He continued to operate even though he lost hundreds of dollars each day he remained open. We were given our full pay, too."

"And wasn't that Cook House something else? We were served meals free of charge whether the mill was running or not."

"Did you ever hear the story of the millman who had been shown through Carson's lumbering operation? He was particularly impressed with the fine quality of food served in the cookhouses, and which seemed to him far above the ordinary. He remarked to Mr. Carson, 'You feed your men entirely too well. Much better than any of the other concerns on the Bay.'

To this Mr. Carson replied, 'You wouldn't use poor coal if you wanted to keep up a good head of steam in your millboilers, would you?' "

What a story! And so typical of this great benefactor.

"I can tell you an experience that happened to me that I'll never forget," said another who had been injured while working in the Carson Woods.

"I was hit by a large redwood, and could not work for months. All that time I received my full pay, and my expenses were paid until I was able to work again. I even received flowers while I was laid up. Don't tell me we won't miss our boss!" And tears filled his eyes as he recounted his experience. "Anyone who would ever try to sue Mr. Carson for damages would be plumb crazy. But no one ever did."

There were many others who gathered down town to talk of this highly esteemed citizen. Business men who operated shipyards, foundries, machine shops, boiler works, tanneries, banks, gas works, furniture factories, pharmacies, grocery stores, etc. These places of business would all be closed on the afternoon of the funeral, and all would attend this most auspicious service.

School children gathered at recess to talk about the great owner of the Castle. They had read about Castles in Spain, but often boasted of Carson's fine castle in their own home town.

"They say he climbed to the top of the tower every day and looked out over the bay and his lumber yards. I wish I could climb that winding stairway just once," remarked a young lad.

"My dad works at the Carson Mill. Maybe he'll be remembered in Mr. Carson's will. Then I can get some new clothes. Wouldn't that be great?"

And so the talk went on and on as the entire city mourned the passing of a great and kind man. The loss and concern united all the citizens, rich and poor, in the foggy, windy town where the largest funeral in their local history was soon to take place. Sadness and excitement were intermingled in the hearts of all.

Interior view of the original Christ Episcopal Church, corner of Fifth and E Streets, Eureka, California.

THE BELL RINGER

The old Christ Episcopal Church that was located at 5th and E Streets, Eureka.

The Carson Mausoleum in Myrtle Grove Cemetery, Eureka, California. (overleaf)

t exactly 1:30 p.m. on Wednesday, Feb. 21, 1912, the clanging bell in the tower of the Christ Episcopal Church began to toll its mournful sound. William Carson, Eureka's most beloved citizen was dead. The church of which he had been a long time member and vestryman was soon to be the scene of one of the most impressive and largest funerals the city had ever known.

As the bell began to toll, the family gathered at the Carson residence, (now the famed Ingomar) ready for a brief private service. The church bell announced the beginning of that family affair. When it was ended, members of the group entered their carriages and proceeded slowly to the church which was located on the corner of 4th and E, not far away. There, thousands of mourners awaited their arrival, as the church bell signalled their approach. The bell was kept ringing for 1¾ hours, silenced only during the services.

The man assigned to ring the bell was a small Victorian gentleman of 41 years, who had washed windows and polished the beautiful carved woodwork in the Carson Mansion. While others drove their fine carriages and approached the service in style, he had left his modest home on 17th and L streets, bidding his wife and two children goodbye, and pedaled his high-seated bicycle, which carried him everywhere he went, to the downtown church. The children he left behind were my brother Melvin, aged 3 and myself, at one year. The bell ringer was Papa. On this memorable day, though hidden in the background, our Papa would occupy a significant position, for he would ring out the sombre tones of the church bell over the entire city. Mama would hear it as she stayed at home with her babies, and her heart would swell with pride. Papa's name was William also—William Caldwell Shuster. He was young and strong, and the bell-ringing would be an easy task physically, though a sad one otherwise. For he too had come in contact with this fine gentleman who was being remembered and honored on this momentous day.

As Papa entered the beautiful church sanctuary with its masses of flowers, he noticed many of the seats in the auditorium were reserved for the hundreds of mill workers who had spent so many years in the logging and lumbering industry under the kind and generous leadership of their highly esteemed boss. In some respects they were a part of Carson's "family," and they were treated as such. They would be assured of places to sit inside while some 2,000 mourners would stand outside in the cold. The church doors would be closed, and those outside would silently await the completion of the service.

After his brief survey, Papa left the sanctuary and took his place in the belfry, ready to begin his once-in-a-lifetime service.

The church was soon filled with people. The family and mourners were seated, the 350 mill workers took their places, and finally the sanctuary was crowded.

As the service began, the bell tones were silenced, and Mama knew the church funeral had begun. The Rev. Shurtleff, a personal friend of Mr. Carson, spoke many kind words about the deceased, who had contributed so generously to the church, and who had often responded to needs presented personally to him by his pastor. His text was taken from Numbers 23:10 — "Let me die the death of the righteous, and let my last end be like his." "The keynote of his eulogy was Mr. Carson as a man, a philanthropist, and a Christian—these being the phases of his character with which Mr. Shurtleff had become familiar." So stated the Humboldt Standard in its evening edition of Feb. 21.

As the service ended and the last strains of the organ played by Mrs. N.C. Libbey, died away,the bell began to toll again as the family, mourners and friends formed the half-mile procession to the Myrtle Grove Cemetery several miles away. Never was there such a parade of carriages, while the monotonous trot of the slow-moving horses only emphasized the great sadness of the day. As the cortege entered the gates of the cemetery, it was an extremely moving experience. Many, however, were forced to remain all along the Myrtle Ave. route.

Along with many others, the cortege included the City officials of Eureka, the directors of the Humboldt Club of which organization Carson had been a life member, and his former employees attending in a body.

A brief service was held at the Carson Mausoleum which had been constructed shortly after the death of Mr. Carson's wife, Sarah, in 1904. Carson's body was placed near that of his wife in the grey cement building, where floral pieces of all kinds were banked about the vault. And finally the fancy, scrolled iron gates were closed and locked.

The funeral was over, the bell in the church steeple was silent, and the mourners moved slowly away—some in one direction, some in another.

The bell-ringer had already slipped away from the empty, silent sanctuary, unnoticed, and slowly and sadly pedaled his way home. He too had learned to love and admire "this heretofore tall, strong man who had seemed to grow more dignified as the years went by. His graying hair and beard had framed a kindly face, and his friendliness to rich and poor alike would be sadly missed." His famed Dolbeer and Carson Mill would continue its operations under the management of his three well-trained sons. And so his work would go on, while the beautiful redwood castle would stand as a silent memorial to a truly great and respected gentleman. The bell-ringer wondered if he would ever enter the castle again. But as he opened the door of his humble dwelling, felt the warmth of the wood stove and smelled the aroma of freshly baked bread just removed from the oven by his lovely wife, he knew he had entered "his castle," and he was satisfied. Tomorrow he would resume his "ordinary" work.

The bell-ringing was over.

61

Historical Note

The "church bell" was actually a chime of five bells, donated by a celebrated Foundry in Troy, N.Y. known as Meneeley and Son. Thomas Walsh, an Irish pioneer resident of Eureka, was responsible for the building of the church in 1869. He raised part of the money when he made a trip to his homeland, and on his way home he ordered the five large bells that make up the chimes. They are now in the Bell Tower of the present Christ Church, a name for which he was responsible. He also brought from England the Communion Silver now on exhibit in the Parish Hall.

The first parish church was a large Victorian style structure at the corner of 4th and E streets, on the edge of the woods that then surrounded the town. The first services were held in that church in May of 1870. The present church building was constructed during the ministry of Charles Leachman, is located on the corner of 15th and H streets, and is one of the loveliest church edifices in our area.

Mama and Papa in front of their home on 17th and L Streets, Eureka.

SUMNER BUILDS
HIS MANSION

11

The Sumner Carson Mansion on 6th and J Streets, Eureka, California, built in 1914.

he year was 1914, and it was time for Sumner to build his dream house. Or was it Amelia's? She had admired a home in San Francisco, very similar to the mansion they finally constructed. And so she supervised the building that became one of the first stucco houses in the area, and then adorned the interior with her own paintings and those of her art teacher, Mr. C.T. Wilson.

Sumner purchased the property on Sixth and J streets in 1909 from Fred Cooper. A beautiful, two story Victorian home had occupied the site. It was built by Eliza and Solomon Cooper in about 1860, parents of Fred Cooper. The gingerbread outlining the roof of the house gave it a lacey look. A green-house was built on one side, in back. No doubt many beautiful homes like this one of the Victorian era, have been torn down and lost to us forever.

Sumner had observed the construction of his father's mansion when he was only twelve. Four years later he had seen the Carson House, now the Pink Lady, built as a wedding present for his brother Milton. In 1912, his father had died, leaving a large inheritance to his daughter and three boys. Sumner had also been working in the Dolbeer Carson Mill, and had been married to Amelia for 14 years. He was now ready to join Amelia in building her "dream house." He employed Mr. Ambrose Foster, who was also the builder of the Carnegie Library and the Eagles Building, and the mansion was begun.

We often picture Amelia as a recluse, not involved much in outside affairs. This was very true in her later years. But at this time she appears to have been very much a part of the designing, furnishing and decorating the stucco mansion, as well as supervising the landscaping of her beautiful yard with roses, rhododendrons, and camellias, many of them imported from Europe. Before the mansion was demolished in 1967, there were over 250 camellia bushes and 300 rhodies. The front walk had been lined with tree roses, while boxwood hedges added to the orderly appearance of the front yard.

Not only so, but all of the electrical fixtures in the house were made from Amelia's original designs and manufactured by the Sechrist Company in Denver, Colorado. Electrical fixtures and appliances were numerous. A dazzling electrolier has been referred to, as well as street-light style lamp posts on the grounds. All were done by the Janssen electric company. Appliances of interest included an electric refrigerator—one of the first two in Humboldt County, the other being purchased by Sumner for his Maple Creek home. Another "first" was a built-in vacuum cleaner system of the commercial type.

No wonder Amelia had stated in her will that her residence be maintained as she had maintained it. She had put her own personality and artistic ability into every part of the mansion.

No doubt Sumner worked with her in the selection of furniture and carpeting—all purchased from Sloans in San Francisco. Some of the carpeting was later replaced by A.C. Gray and Sons, popular Eureka carpet layers. And additional furniture was purchased from Eureka merchant, Mr. Close.

The fish pond was one of Sumner's projects. Beautiful carps, known to be long-lived and cultivated in ponds for their hardy growth and vivid color, were a source of pleasure to both husband and wife. One carp lived in the pond for 35 years, and another lived from the time of construction until 1952. Sumner also enjoyed his huge duck pond at his country estate in Freshwater. He, like his brother Milton, enjoyed outdoor life.

A picture of the home completed in 1914 at an approximate cost of $40,000, gives a very good idea of the exterior. It is surprising that it was not built entirely of redwood, as were the other two mansions. Having been described as a house "ignoring the fads of the age," we can readily see that this was true. No gingerbread, no towers or turrets, no stained glass windows. It was an "individual, beautiful in her own realm."

Entering the Sumner Mansion through the iron gates and beautiful landscaping.

A LEGACY FOR CATS

12

Amelia Carson in her garden.

hen the Times Standard published an account of Amelia Carson's will in January, 1960, nothing attracted the attention of its readers more than the legacy for her much-loved cats. Her estate, valued at $1,191,000 was not surprising. She was a wealthy woman who lived in a three-story mansion, surrounded by spacious lawns and blooming flowers of every hue. Many stories had been circulated about her seclusion—how her last years had been spent in the basement of her well-known mansion. But none were as fantastic as the tales about her cats. When the will was finally made public and curious Eurekans read of the unusual provision made for her pets, they shook their heads in astonishment. Such a thing was unheard of. The will stipulated that 1600 shares of American Tobacco Company Stock would be left to provide for the care of the cats. And the will further provided that the estate was not to be distributed as long as the cats were alive.

"The cats had been Amelia Carson's first love," said Mr. Roy Tanner who had been her gardener for 37 years. He had lived in the mansion for three years after Amelia's death, while the estate was being settled.

When the will was ruled illegal according to state law, most of the cats were disposed of. However, Roy kept one named Tabby, who lived to be a very old cat.

Amelia's constant loving care of the cats was almost unbelievable. But what does an older lady do in a huge mansion, alone except for a housekeeper when she can no longer get around without great difficulty, or walk through her garden and enjoy the massive rhododendrons, the trim tree-roses lining her front walk, and her choice varieties of dahlias? She had her doll collection from all over the world. Some were life-size with human hair. I saw them sitting around in her living room on one of my visits as a child. She owned a button collection which evidently fascinated her—at least for awhile. But these were not living and breathing, and gave her no companionship. And besides all that, she had no children.

I visited her after she had moved to the basement. I was ushered in by her housekeeper, Mrs. Bruce Heckman, nicknamed Gussie. My little son and I approached her as she sat in a big leather chair in front of the huge wood furnace that supplied heat to the entire house. She had moved there during the war, and some thought she may have been fearful—perhaps of bombings. Also, she had reached the point where she could no longer climb the stairs to the bedroom and bath area. The basement had been remodelled years earlier and made into a comfortable apartment for a Philippino cook, named Hilarion. Few people probably knew this.

As we visited with Mrs. Carson, I noticed "Gussie" standing by a meat block, cutting choice round steak into small bite-sized pieces. I know it was choice meat which had been carefully trimmed of all fat and sinews. This was a "must" as Amelia ordered her meat from a local butcher shop regularly. My husband, a meat-cutter, knows very well how particular she was, for he supplied her with meat for awhile.

After the steak was prepared, small tin dishes would be spread on the floor, into which portions of meat were placed—a dish for each cat. This was regular routine in the Carson Mansion. No wonder Amelia was concerned about the welfare of her cats after she was gone.

How many cats she had at one time, and where they came from I do not know. It has been reported that there were 20 cats in the house when she died. But I interviewed Mr. Lee Dowd, another housekeeper, shortly after the house was demolished, and he gave me more information. He said there were approximately 70 cats buried in the orchard on the "K" street side. These were buried individually in galvanized tin boxes about 2 ft. long, 18 in. high, and 14-16 in. wide. The cats were wrapped in baby blankets, and the boxes sealed by Mr. Bruce Heckman, a tinsmith and husband of Gussie, the meat cutter for the cats.

Some of the cats were stored in the attic. Seventeen boxes were found there after Amelia's death. Some folks, anxious to find hidden jewels, wanted to get to the tin boxes and open them. Mr. Tanner said that if there had been any jewelry buried, it would have been with her two special cats, Felix and Bobby. There was none. Neither was there money or jewels found between the mansion walls, as some suspected and searched for.

As I watched the demolition of the home that Mrs. Carson had dreamed would someday be a museum, and watched huge "cats" destroying the very grounds where the pet cats sunned themselves in specially prepared "fenced-in areas," and where small pools of water had been spaced around the grounds for the accommodation of thirsty cats; and later learned that their burial grounds had been torn up, and the tin boxes scattered all about—I experienced a sense of utter destruction and almost lack of regard for the wishes of a lonely woman who thought she had taken care of it all. Even her pink, purple and red rhodies, her immaculate lawn, and her carefully trimmed boxwood hedge were being mercilessly uprooted and crushed by the giant "cats"—the caterpillar tractors.

The entire scene was inconceivable and incongruous. And the barren mansion, stripped of its beauty—it too was succumbing to the mighty blows of the massive ball that would soon leave nothing but useless debris to be hauled away by heavy dump trucks—merely hired to do a job. It would soon be over, and the will that had been so carefully prepared, now over-ruled and declared illegal; the will that had provided a handsome legacy for her cats, would be remembered only in the pages of history as a foolish whim of a solitary old lady, who had been shut away in a very quiet mansion.

Papa, Roy Tanner, Hilarion and Lee Dowd.

Papa and Hilarion, the Philippino cook.

THE AUCTION

ALL INTERIOR FINISH TRIM

NO LIMIT	NO RESERVE

SPECIAL PUBLIC

AUCTION

SUMNER CARSON MANSION

6th & J Sts. ● Eureka, Calif.
Fri., June 16 ● 1 p.m.

House open for inspection Thursday 12-4

PARTIAL LISTING

CARVED MOLDINGS ● ALL TRIMS ● PILLARS ● BEAM CEILING ● CURVED BEVELED PLATE GLASS DOORS ● PLATE GLASS WINDOWS ● BEAUTIFUL STAIR CASE ● FIREPLACE MANTLE ● MARBLE ● SLIDING DOORS ● CARPETS ● DRAPES ● BATHROOM FIXTURES including VITREOUS PEDESTAL, SINKS, BATHTUBS, TOILET & TANKS, SHOWER (sprays from all angles; you've never seen one like it) ● KITCHEN & WARDROBE GLASS DOORS ● RELIEFS ON TWO BUILDINGS ● HOT HOUSE ● 2 GARAGE DOORS.

All beautifully preserved and easily removed.
Plan to attend this once in a lifetime sale!

TERMS CASH ● BID & BUY

Everything will be sold where is and as is. Cost and responsibility of removal of purchase will remain with the purchaser.

TWO DAYS TO REMOVE MERCHANDISE FROM PREMISES

Carl Johnson Co.; Auctioneer DON JOHNSON
For further information call 443-4851.

13

A view from the front entrance, as trucks haul away the furnishings.

Newspaper clipping about the auction — June 1967. (overleaf)

he time had come to dispose of the long vacant mansion. It could no longer stand useless and empty with no future in sight. The decision was made to strip the once elegant home of all that remained beautiful, and then destroy it completely, clearing the site for a new, modern building.

On Thursday, June 15, 1967 the Sumner Carson Mansion was opened to the public for inspection. An auction of all interior finish trim, glass doors and windows, pillars, bathroom fixtures, etc. would be held the following day. The newspaper called it a "once in a lifetime sale". And so it was. Two days would be given to remove everything salable from the premises—Friday and Saturday—that was all. For on Monday, the 18th, the remains of the desolate mansion would be totally demolished. The Carl Johnson Company with auctioneer Don Johnson would be in charge of the Friday sale, and Bill Smith, local crane operator, would superintend the demolition.

The mansion was built in 1914 and completed in 1919 at a cost of $40,000. Sumner resided in the home for about twenty-five years—about the same length of time that his father had lived in his mansion—while Amelia remained for a total of forty-five years. William, the father, never saw his son's mansion, for it was not begun until two years after his death. When Amelia died, the home was left to two nieces who originally sold it to a private individual, Harold Chittenden, for $200,000. He planned to convert it into a museum. However he was killed in a plane wreck, and Amelia's dream died with him. Finally the mansion was sold to the Times Standard Publishing Company for the same price. The sale was completed on April 4, 1967.

By that time the mansion had stood empty for ten years. Beautiful carpets had become moth-eaten, and heavy velvet draperies worn and faded. It had been opened to the community in 1961 when there were two showings. Two thousand dollars were received at the first exhibit and twenty-five hundred at the second. All funds were donated to charity.

Later, the home was sold to Mr. Bill Smith and the interior was purchased by Mr. Ernest Pierson, local builder, from Mr. Smith.

The auction was in progress as I entered the double front doors with their arched panes of plate glass. They stood wide open as prospective buyers stepped inside onto bare hardwood floors. In the once elegant living room where I, as a child, had seen life-size dolls sitting around in the overstuffed furniture stood the auctioneer disposing of beautifully carved mahogany pillars, ornate fireplace decorations, doors and window-casings. As I saw men carrying out huge wooden pieces, I wondered what I could buy as a keepsake from the mansion that held memories because of Papa.

I could see the music room beyond where Amelia's Steinway Grand Piano, played by Amelia in her younger years and later by her good friend, Julia Gall, was now only a memory. The music was gone, while the monotonous voice of the experienced auctioneer echoed throughout the empty rooms.

In the kitchen there was a scene of feverish activity. This room had been remodelled following a fire which took place after Papa's death. At that time a large electric range had been moved in to replace the old wood stove. It too, was missing. The now bare cupboards that had been a part of the new addition were being jerked from the walls by eager buyers who would soon haul them away to their own kitchens. And the once immaculate floor scrubbed by Papa regularly after the ritual of cat-feeding was now covered with debris. Thus the "invasion" continued.

The spacious dining room with its sturdy oak trim would

soon be completely dismantled. The long dining table I had once seen displaying Amelia's Christmas gifts—and among them a small piece of china from Papa—was gone, as were also the lovely green and bronze Tiffany chandelier overhead, and the lush green carpet. Both had found a home in the Clarke Museum in Eureka. Only the tall windows from floor to high ceiling let in a cheering light. They too, would soon be removed and the mansion would be left windowless and naked.

But the nostalgia remained. Had not Papa entered and cleaned every room in the house? Had he not escorted me away up in the attic even against Amelia's wishes, because "he worked there"? A beautiful piano, stored on the third floor, had been removed through the roof and lowered by crane before the auction and purchased by a Mr. Denninger. It must have been moved up there to make room for the Steinway Grand in the music room, sold to Jim Mearns of Humboldt State University for $1,500.00 but now valued at $10 or $15 thousand.

What keepsake could I carry home? So far I had seen nothing that would satisfy my desire. I left the busy scene and stepped outside. There, by the side of the house was a huge crane with a man standing aloft, removing decorative trim from around the top of the mansion. He was taking down small sections, some measuring about three feet in length, made of cement with a scroll design. I purchased a piece for $3.00. I later learned that all of this relief work was done by James Hubbard, uncle of Homer Fisher of Bayside, whom I interviewed. Some of the work was hand-carved, and some had been cast in hand-made molds. It had taken Hubbard one and one-half years to complete the task.

I had nothing of any great value—only a small remembrance of a once stately mansion. It was enough—a humble piece of trim—humble like Papa.

For the next two days cars and trucks pulled up beside the ravished structure and literally hauled away the "beauty of the interior". No doubt many homes in our city today have their rooms decorated with mahogany and oak trim, with cupboards and windows and doors from the Sumner Carson Mansion, as the occupants speak proudly of the "once in a lifetime" auction in which they were privileged to participate. They, too, have their keepsakes.

A crane outside the Mansion.

I Saw
A Mansion
Demolished

The lonely fireplace in the attic.

They're going to kill it! I watch killing on T.V. That's what they're going to do!" These startling words were uttered by a small boy standing near me as we witnessed the demolition of the once elegant Sumner Carson Mansion.

On Monday morning, June 19, 1967, I drove to the already stripped mansion on 6th and "J" streets, and parked my car at 9:00 a.m. outside the front entry. I had been strangely drawn to the devastating scene, and as the work proceeded, I kept a detailed account of the intensive job of destroying one of Eureka's most beautiful landmarks. The home had been described as "a house representing Eureka, a town of unparalleled profusion of architecture." It was further compared to an "individual, beautiful in her own realm, ignoring the fads of the age."

However beautiful it had been, it was now a scene of disaster. The house stood naked in the midst of a yard that had been robbed of its beauty by a huge bulldozer. Torn up soil with boxwood hedges gone, trash piled high in the back yard, two gigantic palm trees soon to be uprooted, and desolation everywhere. Ivy that had clung to the walls for many years had been ripped off, revealing the cracked gray stucco underneath. Windows deprived of their glass panes seemed to stare at us with empty sockets. The roof lay bare of its colorful red tile. Iron gates with their graceful scroll designs no longer stood guard to intruders. Lamp posts whose warm lights shone through the night and offered protection and comfort to Amelia in her old age were now missing.

I watched the activity inside. Two remaining entrance doors stood open. I could see ladders set up in the once well-furnished rooms. Last-minute jobs were being completed before the final destruction. Men were removing the carved mahogany staircase that once graced the entrance hall, winding its way to the second floor. White marble was being chiselled from the deserted entry. A fire chief arrived to make an inspection, and a TV camera man appeared. Finally one remaining carpenter came into sight making a last examination with his flashlight.

The only activity outside was that of the giant bulldozer still digging around the palm trees on either side in front.

Cars drove slowly by, while curious and concerned onlookers gazed at the sad scene. It looked as if a wild animal had been turned loose and destroyed everything in sight—a monster.

At 12:15 the demolition apparatus began to arrive. A huge crane from the Eureka Crane Service, with Bill Smith as operator, drove in. By 1:20 the crane lifted the roof from the North porch to facilitate the removal of the stately cement pillars supporting it. I was impressed with the careful, orderly procedure.

The work seemed to proceed very slowly, as if the workers were trying to postpone the sad job they had been called upon to do.

Some of the last articles to be removed from the desolate house were the radiators—a huge one which had been located under the mahogany stairway, was laboriously carried out by four men. Then to my surprise I saw a small radiator literally tossed out an upstairs window on my left, and soon another on my right. And finally, at 2:55 the crane lifted an extra-large rectangular bathtub through a second story window. To my knowledge this was the last article to be removed. The inside work was finished, the carpenters left, and the final load of salvageable material was hauled away. The interior of the mansion, once grandly furnished, had been completely razed and was now "ready" for the final blows.

That evening as Dick De Witt, TV newsman reported the day's activities, he re-echoed the feeling of the little boy, when he said, "The old gal is going to be hard to kill." Yes, to young and old alike it would certainly be a real killing.

On Tuesday morning I arrived on the "K" Street side at 9:00 to continue my observation. A cat was already at work removing broken cement, shrubbery and other debris from the yard. The palm trees were still being uprooted. The growth of years had spread their roots deep and wide, while the trees stood as sentinels in the wind, fog, rain and sunshine. Until now they had been secure.

I noted Carl Johnson's truck on hand, as another trucker, Harry Sanderson, hauled away more debris. A bystander commented, "Isn't it sad? I think they should have kept it for a museum or something."

By 9:45 more pillars were being removed from the north porch. The roof that had been lifted by the crane was being sustained by pieces of timber. The ornate tops were separated from the pillars and offered at $30.00 apiece. Mr. Ernest Pierson had reserved some of them, along with the interior staircase, panellings and pillars for his new bank building on the Harris Street Mall, and for the Roos Atkins modern store in the same area.

A huge crane from Mercer Fraser Co. was now on hand with an accumulation ball of 3000 lbs. ready to swing the death blows.

I missed a few hours here, as I drove to the Clarke Memorial Museum and talked to Carl Ekaas, the curator. He told me that William Carson's home had the architecture, but that Sumner's had the furnishings. He showed me some colorful Tiffany chandeliers from the 7th Street mansion, and told me of plans to set up a room with some of its appointments.

When I returned at 4:30 the kitchen, dining room, most of the music room and part of the attic were gone, leaving the remaining structure exposed like a huge doll house split wide open. Destruction had certainly begun.

On Wednesday morning at 10:15, the crew was further demolishing the rear of the house as I drove up. It was a cold windy day—and to me, an eerie atmosphere prevailed. As usual, onlookers gathered, hardly believing what they saw. Children out of school were especially attracted. Old timers, neighbors and newsmen looked on. I recognized Herb Quaintance, local nurseryman; Claire Otis, newspaper man; and Nina Hartman, close neighbor with her mother from New York.

At 3:00 p.m. the attic was attacked, as the Mercer Fraser crane swung its massive demolition ball into the topmost room of the crumbling landmark. The torn brown burlap which had lined the attic walls was blowing about in a ghastly manner. And as the weight of the ball crashed into the roof, clouds of black dust poured out, while gusts of wind blew it into our upturned faces. It was an accumulation of soot from the old wood furnace that had consumed 25 cords of wood each year.

A strange emotional climate prevailed—that cloudy June day. Some onlookers laughed, some cried, while others stood and stared—almost shocked into silence. Even a huge monkey tree in the back yard seemed to wave its arms hopelessly. A covered well remained isolated. On top of the proud old mansion, a cupola with its skylight, leaned crazily sideways, while a tall gray chimney still stood upright.

Meanwhile the destructive claws of the cat pried into the piles of debris growing larger and larger, closing in on one load, dumping it into a waiting truck, and reaching for another. The rhythm went on and on.

Soon the brick attic fireplace stood exposed. It seemed to be the last remaining feature of the interior yet intact. It was a lonely sight—made of used bricks with its arched opening and wide hearth. Destruction gained momentum as entire walls and floors crashed and fell at one blow. I asked myself, "How many blows can that top story stand?" Blow after blow and the top quivered. And then more black dust. The work continued throughout the dreary afternoon.

I noticed Mrs. Bruce Heckman—Gussie as she had been called—the lady who had so faithfully cut the meat and fed the cats. She walked by, barely glancing at the scene, and went on.

On other days I had seen Mr. Wm. Hiscox, Sr., local contractor; Merle Shuster, TV camera man; and wives of the crane operators. These were but a few of the observers.

On Thursday morning the crane had stopping working on

the depleted structure. Attention was focused on the final uprooting of the palms in front. What a mammoth job it was! The tree on the north side, weighing 30 tons, was carefully loaded by crane onto an exceedingly long truck driven by Walt Waldkirch from Arcata. He pulled out for McKinleyville at 1:35 P.M. At 3:00, the tree on the south side, weighing 40 tons was loaded. Mr. M.D. Letz of McKinleyville, brother of movie star, George Montgomery, was having them moved to his ranch. I asked him how much it was costing him to move the trees. His only reply was "Plenty."

"Do you think they will live?" I continued.

"I sure hope so," he said.

I hoped so too.

The yard work continued. At 3:00 the giant rhododendrons that had bloomed so profusely in the front garden were plowed up. They had been a source of beauty and great attraction to all who passed by, and were one of the most massive displays in our city where the climate is so conducive to their growth. And because of their abundance, Eureka has celebrated their beauty in an annual Rhododendron Festival and Parade. Whereas, in the early 1900's when sweet peas were prevalent, the Sweet Pea Parade was a yearly feature.

Leaving the scene, I drove homeward, intending to be on hand for the final destruction the next morning. As I drove up the "K" Street side on Friday at 9:45, I saw, to my great disappointment, that I had not been there to witness the end. The mansion was gone, and I, her most faithful mourner, had not been there to see her disappear. Before 9:00 a.m. the last remains had been destroyed, although dump trucks were still hauling away the seemingly endless debris. The fine old historic mansion was no more. It had taken scarcely more than four days to remove from existence forever the Carson home of fifty years, that might have stood a century or more. Amelia's dream of preserving it as a museum had been shattered.

And now my story of the Carson family—and more particularly of Sumner—has come to an end. Papa had been associated with the family for over fifty years. The close friendship of Sumner and Papa, the afternoon coffee breaks enjoyed by Amelia and Papa, and the many hours of work he spent at the mansion, give my story a nostalgic touch. In my imagination, I see again a small, Victorian, aging gentleman riding away on his bicycle to his humble home on Sixth Street near Myrtle Avenue. The floors have been mopped, the windows washed, the silverware polished, and the porches cleaned. His work is ended, as he, too, fades out of the picture.

Still, "The Castle," the beautiful Ingomar, defying earthquake and storm, and admired by tourists from all over the world continues to be a source of great pride to the citizens of Eureka, California, U.S.A.

The demolition of the Sumner Carson Mansion in June, 1967.

BRINGING
THE INGOMAR
UP TO DATE

15

Snow on the Mansion — taken January 25, 1950.

he Ingomar Club, incorporated in April 1950, is now thirty-four years old. The mansion was bought from Clarence and Sarah Bell La Boyteaux for $35,000, $10,000 of which was paid for the furnishings. Sarah Bell was the granddaughter of William Carson. Carl Gustafson, local auto dealer, and J.H. Crouthers, newspaper publisher, approached 65 local business men with the goals of obtaining the mansion and finding local people to contribute to the purchase and form a club. The plan worked and the mansion became the property of the future club. The only provision made by the La Boyteauxs was that the structure be maintained for at least ten years. And maintained it has been, even though it costs $35,000—exactly the original cost—to paint it alone. It has been painted three times since the club organized. The colors have changed very little.

The mansion is kept in tip-top condition. Although very much like the original, a few additions have been made, including a new dining hall constructed in 1955 to accommodate the 250 local members and 50 non-resident men, and a green canopy over the front entrance.

More recently, new red carpeting has been laid on the grand stairway and the hallways on the first and second floors. The two front rooms have just been carpeted in a lovely beige. The family dining room has been re-carpeted and the employees' dining room is completely renovated. George Herd restored the wood, re-stained it, and has painted beautiful scenic murals on the walls. The Ingomar is closed for two weeks annually for general upkeep and for staff vacations.

The name "Ingomar" comes from the play "Ingomar the Barbarian" which Carson had seen in San Francisco and liked so well he named his downtown theatre after it. Since the La Boyteauxs would not allow the club to use the Carson name, it was suggested by Ritchie Woods to use Ingomar. And so the name was adopted, although the names Victorian Club, Castle Club and Harbor Club had also been suggested.

In December 1970 the club celebrated its 20th Anniversary, and on February 24, 1983 the members had a party to honor 23 remaining Charter members from the original 118. Members honored were:

Kelton Steele, Ernest Pierson, Merced Wrigley, Herman Bistrin, Kenny Johnson, Francis Matthews, Dr. Stan Schmidt, Bill S. Mullen, Henry Terheyden, Wayne Vickers, Dr. Sam Burre, Walter Thoreson, Andrew Rosaia, Dr. Max Goodman, Milt Huber, Earl Cannam Jr., and Barney Barnard.

The Ingomar is preserved and operated by one housekeeper, one gardener, one maintenance man, one chef along with a relief chef, and two book-keepers. The new manager, Alan Marsh, resides in the apartment above the carriage house.

The gardener, George Herd has recently lived on a sailboat in the Eureka Boat Basin with his wife Grace. Both are from Scotland. Now they have purchased a home. Grace began her career in the Ingomar as a kitchen helper, then took over as housekeeper, and is now head waitress. On Sept. 1, 1982 George became the gardener. A very talented artist, he also makes flower arrangements for the mansion, and is now engaged in building a greenhouse. He sounds like a man who really enjoys his work.

Mr. Jack F. Daly, Jr. is president of the club and meets with his board of directors once each month. Dr. Stan Schmidt is chairman of the Historical Committee.

Ingomar membership is restricted to men who are interested in "good fellowship, the fine arts, and athletic events." Dominoes is a favorite game. Women are allowed at week-end dinners and special events.

A present display of historical documents and information, original deeds and old pictures, located on the second floor, has been of interest to members and friends.

In spite of signs indicating "Private Property, No Trespassing!" strays find their way into the grounds, peer into windows, and even ring the front doorbell. The old saying is true: "Fools (still) rush in where angels fear to tread."

A Castle
In Fairyland

Conclusion

The Carson Mansion in lights.

ave you ever seen a castle in Fairyland? Well, I have. Only this one was real! It was a tall mansion with towers and turrets, pillars and gables all lighted with hundreds of twinkling Christmas lights of many colors. My husband and I were on our way to our company Christmas dinner held annually at Aldo's Italian Restaurant just around the corner, when all of a sudden, there it was—a fairyland spectacular, right before our eyes. We had seen the Carson Mansion many times in its Victorian beauty but on this festive evening we viewed it in an entirely different setting. The familiar and varied outlines of this world-renowned redwood castle were clothed in soft ethereal balls of light which transformed the entire scene into a Christmas miracle—beautiful beyond description. Instantly I was being transported into the dream world of my childhood days when fairy tales brightened my life with visions of fantasy—kings and queens, princes and princesses in royal splendor. And I became young again in the gala spirit of the enchanting Season.

There was another occasion when the same Castle became a living reality of a very favorite fairy tale—Cinderella. It was an exciting evening as my husband and I, along with three other invited couples drove to the Mansion, passed through the open, decorative iron gates as if we had been given a pass to the "royal palace"—gates that had been closed to us for nearly seventy years. In that magical moment, I felt like Cinderella going to the ball. We followed the circular driveway around the fabulous house to the side entrance and entered the hall near the new and modern dining room. We understood that the massive double front doors opening behind a spacious porch supported by ornamented pillars, were closed to the public for safety reasons. We entered the hallway and hung our coats in a nearby closet, ready for a tour of the entire eighteen room mansion.

Mr. and Mrs. Newton Steward, our host and hostess for the evening, were our gracious escorts through the elegant rooms. They were members of the Ingomar Club. It should be explained that only members could invite guests, while only on Sunday evenings were women permitted. We women in our formal gowns and the men in dress suits and ties had no difficulty in climbing the wide carpeted stairway to the second floor. Nor did we hesitate to proceed to the third floor with its once prominent ball-room. However, the ascent to the observation tower by a narrow, spiral stairway was a little more difficult with our high heels and long dresses. But none of us lost a glass slipper. This time the twinkling lights of the city of Eureka, the moving headlights of the cars, and flashing neon signs added to the beauty and fascination of the evening.

As we returned to the lovely dining room and settled around a large circular table, we were seated by Elizabeth Steward who arranged us in English fashion, husbands and wives apart. We studied the menus and ordered our favorite entrees before proceeding to the largest and most fantastic buffet table we had ever seen. It stretched nearly the entire length of the room and was complete with salads, hors d'oeuvres, pickled shrimp, fresh shrimp, fresh crab, smoked oysters, herring, peppers, pickles, salami, cheeses, and fruits—more than we could possibly sample. As we filled our plates and returned to the dining table we heard tales of China and the experiences of the Stewards who had lived there for many years. With such good company and appetizing food, the evening passed all too quickly.

But as Cinderella must hurry and leave before midnight, so we too must make haste for our Sunday evening service at the church, especially since our pastor and wife Rev. & Mrs. Edgar Parker were among the guests. Back again in our "carriages" we drove through the beautiful landscaped yard, and out into the everyday world of reality. But we did not leave our fantasy behind. For as we drove to the church and entered in our formal gowns, we could not shed the glow and enchantment of our wonderful evening. And I reposed in the joy of it all night long.

The Fantasy still exists. Today people from all over the world come to our city to view and photograph the Carson Mansion. As they drive through the streets of Old Town, and pass aged store fronts now bright with paint and revived with business activity, drive over brick streets, lighted at night with antique street lights, there comes into view at the end of Second Street a sight beyond description—a castle complete with all the gingerbread, towers and turrets, stained glass windows, porches, and Victorian artistry one could imagine. And it is uniquely ours—preserved in all its original beauty— for all the world to see and enjoy. Benjamin Sacks has appropriately described it as "a fairyland of architectural wonderment." It is still my "castle in fairyland."

The End

Important Dates

1825 William Carson, son of Charles Carson and Jane Baldwin, born in New Brunswick, July 15.

1833 Sarah Wilson, later to become Mrs. William Carson, born in New Brunswick, January 4.

1849 William Carson, 24 years old, embarked on "The Brazilian" from New Brunswick.

1850 William arrived in San Francisco in April, after a 6 month's voyage.

1850 William arrived in Eureka, age 25.

1862 Partnership of William Carson and John Dolbeer formed.

1864 William Carson and Sarah Wilson married in San Francisco. William, 39, Sarah, 31.

1865 John Milton born.

1867 Carlotta born.

1872 Amelia Emily Ohman, later to become Sumner Carson's wife, born in Eureka, May 21.

1873 Sumner Carson born in Eureka, Nov. 6.

1875 Bay Mill constructed by Carson and Dolbeer.

1877 William Carson Jr. born to William and Sarah.

1878 Carson and Dolbeer's first mill burned.

1883 William Carson shut down his huge sawmill.

1885-6 The Great Mansion was built.

1888 The first street cars in Eureka.

100

1889	The Carson House built by William as a wedding present for his son, Milton.
1890	The Carson block built—N.E. corner of 3rd and F. Also, the Ingomar Theatre—2nd and 3rd floors.
1890	Sumner joined the Gold Rush to Alaska.
1900	Wedding of Sumner Carson and Amelia Ohman.
1902	Death of John Dolbeer.
1904	Death of Mrs. William Carson, May 7.
1912	Death of William Carson, Feb. 19. Nearly 87.
1912	Carson House (Milton's home) leased and sold.
1914	Sumner Carson Mansion on 6th and J built.
1919	First showing of the Valley of the Giants with scenes from the interiors of both mansions.
1924	Modern electric mill built under Milton's supervision. Complete junking of Dolbeer and Carson Mill.
1933	Wedding Anniversary of Milton and wife in the big Mansion.
1937	Death of William W. Carson, youngest son of William, at age 60.
1938	Death of Sumner Carson at age 65.
1940	Last day of the street cars in Eureka, Feb. 20.
1941	Death of Milton Carson at 76.
1944	Death of Milton's wife, Mary Bell.
1950	Carson Mill acquired by Pacific Lumber Co. of Scotia-- ended the 96 year old firm.

1950	Carson Mansion sold to 70 Eureka business men, and the Ingomar Club incorporated in April 1950.
1951	Carson House, across from the mansion, bought by Lloyd Bridges and Frank Smith.
1957	Death of Sumner's wife, Amelia at 85.
1964	Carson House purchased by Robert Madsen and Milton Ragsdale, Jr.
1967	Sumner Carson Mansion demolished, June 15.
1968	Completion of $2 million Times Standard building constructed on the site of the Sumner Carson Mansion.

BIBLIOGRAPHY

1. The Day Books—William C. Shuster

2. Carson Mansion and Ingomar Theatre—Benjamin Sacks

3. Local Newspapers
   Weekly Standard from 1873
   Times Weekly Telephone from 1885
   Humboldt Times
   Humboldt Standard
   Times Standard

4. Humboldt Historian—from 1930 to 1982

5. History of Humboldt County by Irvine

6. The Carson Mansion—Courtesy of Eureka and Humboldt County Chamber of Commerce

7. Redwood and Lumbering in California Forests
   Edgar Cherry and Co.

8. Susie Baker Fountain Papers

9. North Coast Outdoors—"The Passing of a Lady"
   July 28, 1967

10. Women's Circle Magazine—April 1968, page 45

11. Clarke's Museum—old newspapers

12. Interviews:
    1. Edmund Baldwin
    2. Lee Dowd
    3. Karl Ekaas
    4. Homer Fisher
    5. Roy Tanner

13. Libraries
    Humboldt County Library—Historical Room
    Humboldt State University—Historical Room

CREDITS